EASIEST 5-FINGER PIANO COLLECTION

Chart Hits

15 popular chart hits arranged for 5-finger piano

Wise Publications
part of The Music Sales Group
London / New York / Paris / Sydney / Copenhagen / Berlin / Madrid / Tokyo

CHASING PAVEMENTS

Words & Music by Francis White & Adele Adkins

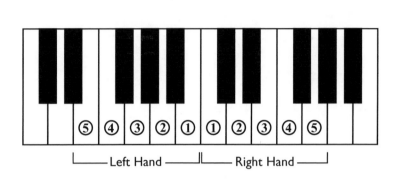

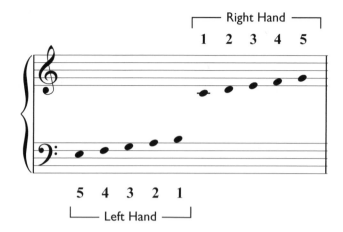

Expressively and steadily ♩ = 80

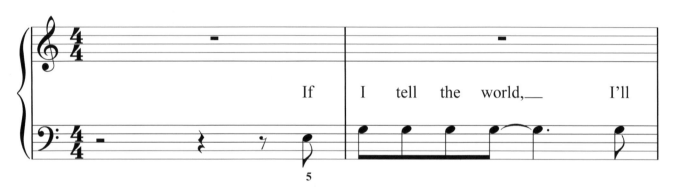

If I tell the world,___ I'll

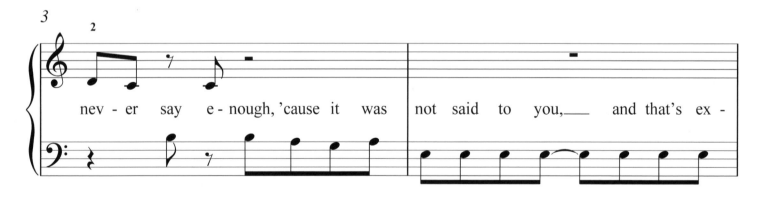

nev - er say e - nough, 'cause it was not said to you,___ and that's ex -

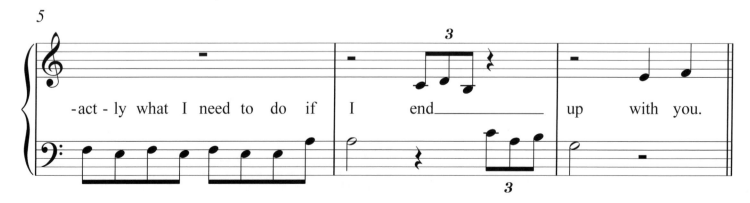

-act - ly what I need to do if I end_____ up with you.

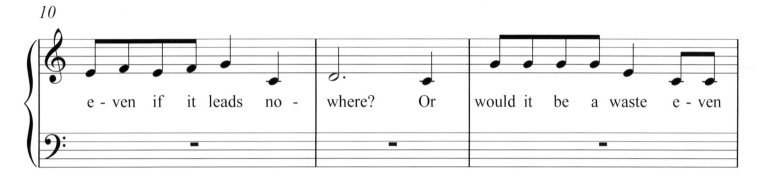

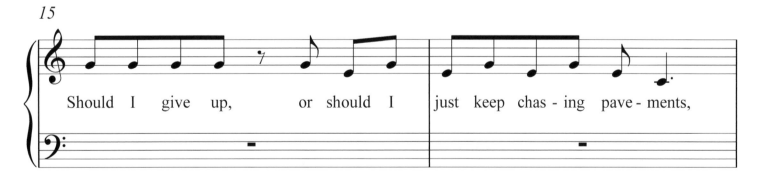

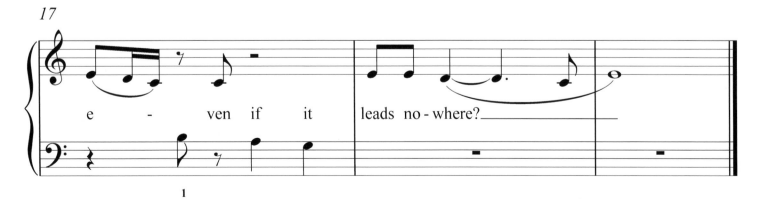

SOMEWHERE ONLY WE KNOW

Words & Music by Tim Rice-Oxley, Tom Chaplin & Richard Hughes

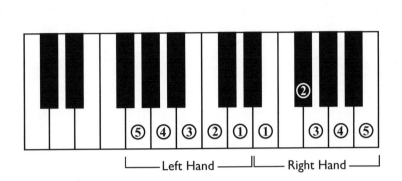

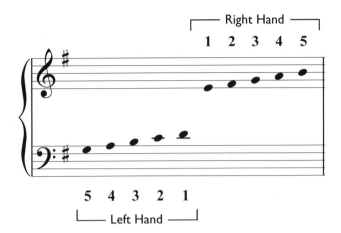

Steadily ♩ = 84

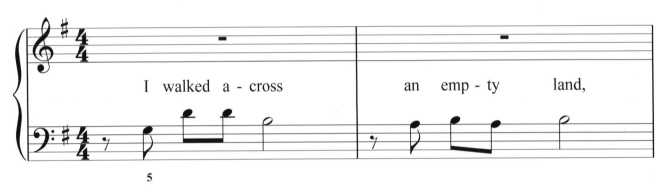

I walked a-cross an emp-ty land,

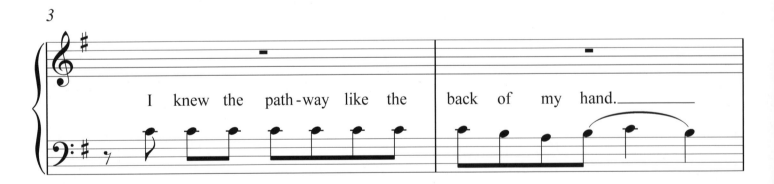

I knew the path-way like the back of my hand.

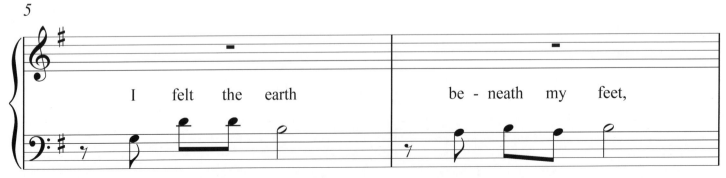

I felt the earth be-neath my feet,

ABOUT YOU NOW

Words & Music by Cathy Dennis & Lukasz Gottwald

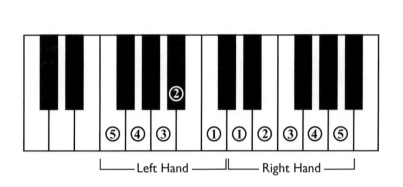

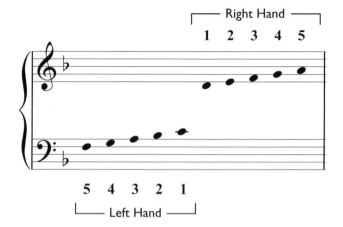

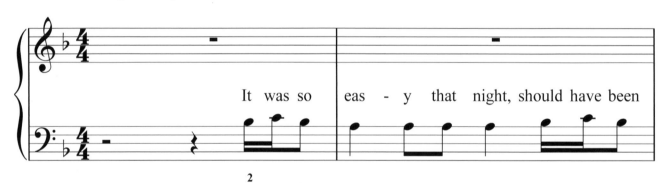

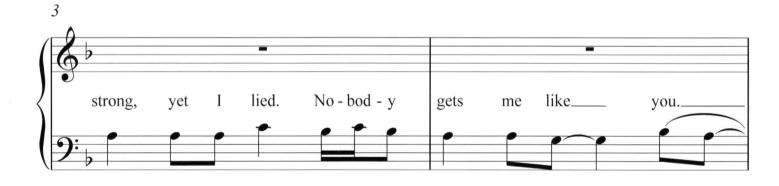

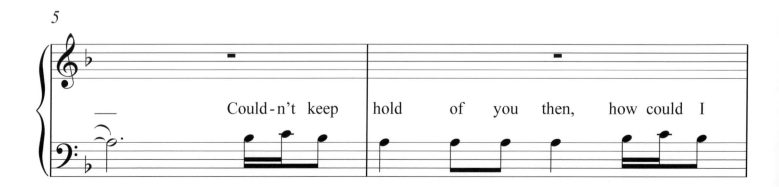

OTHER SIDE OF THE WORLD

Words & Music by KT Tunstall & Martin Terefe

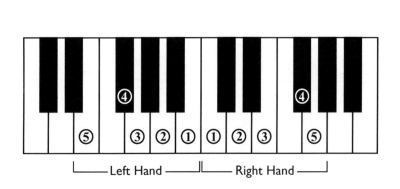

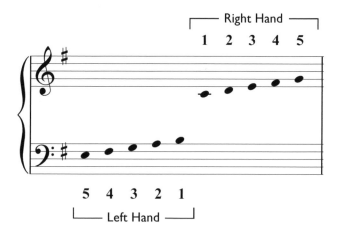

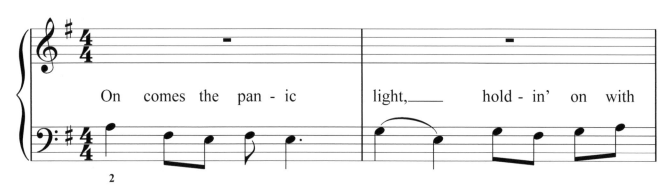

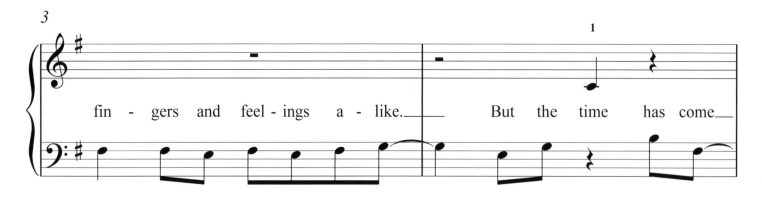

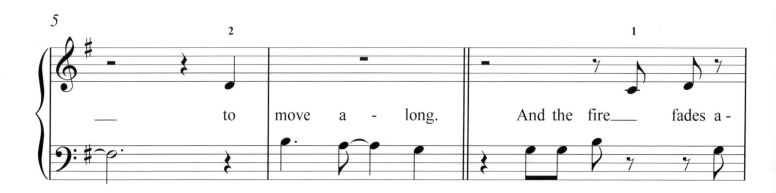

YOU GIVE ME SOMETHING

Words & Music by Francis White & James Morrison

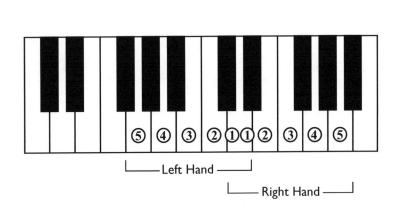

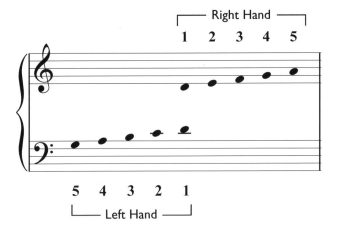

You on-ly stay with me in the morn-ing,

you on-ly hold me when I sleep.   I was meant to tread the

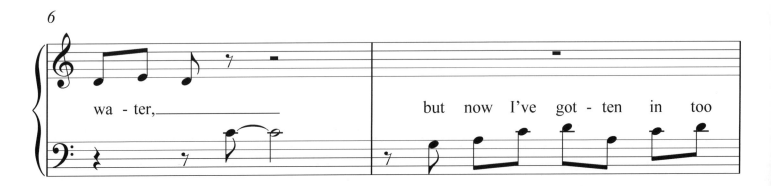

wa-ter,   but now I've got-ten in too

SHINE

Words & Music by Mark Owen, Gary Barlow, Stephen Robson, Jason Orange & Howard Donald

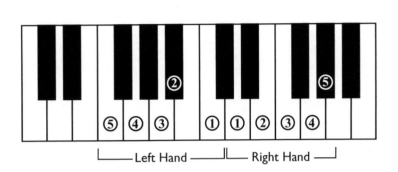

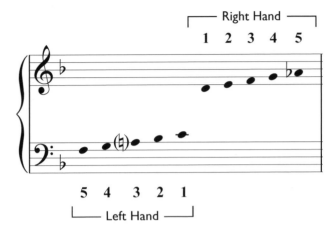

Brightly, with a bounce ♩ = 88

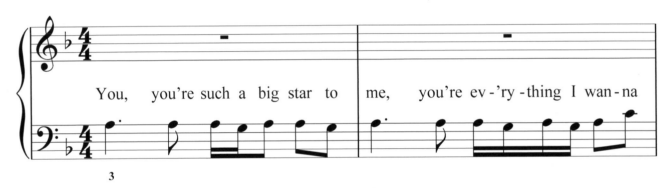

You, you're such a big star to me, you're ev-'ry-thing I wan-na

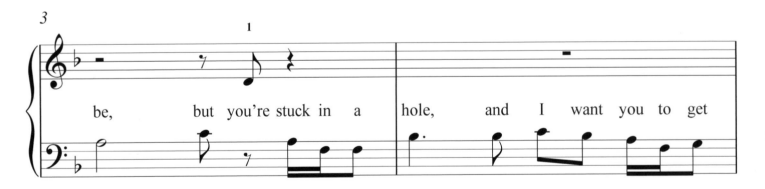

be, but you're stuck in a hole, and I want you to get

out, out, out, all your an-ti-ci-pa-tion pulls you

NEVER HAD A DREAM COME TRUE

Words & Music by Cathy Dennis & Simon Ellis

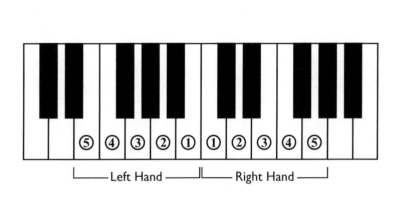

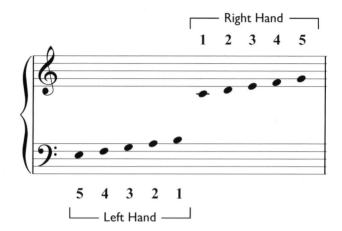

Ev-'ry-bod-y's got some-thing they had to leave be-hind.

One re-gret from yes-ter-day___ that just seems to grow with time.___ There's no

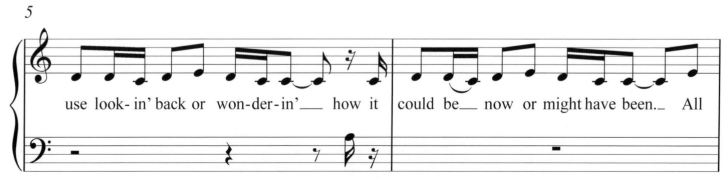

use look-in' back or won-der-in'___ how it could be___ now or might have been.___ All

UMBRELLA

Words & Music by Christopher Stewart, Terius Nash, Shawn Carter & Thaddis Harrell

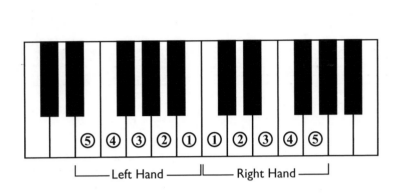

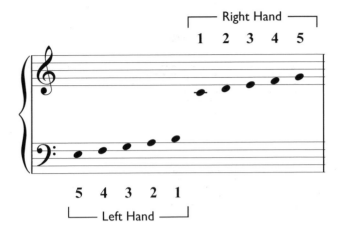

FOUNDATIONS

Words & Music by Kate Nash & Paul Epworth

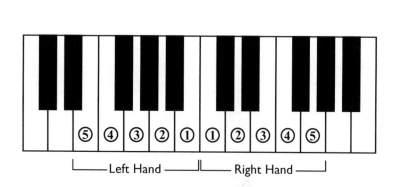

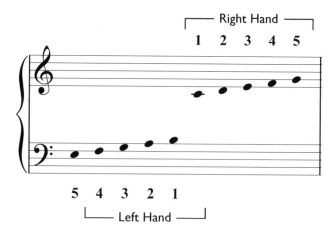

Briskly ♩ = 144

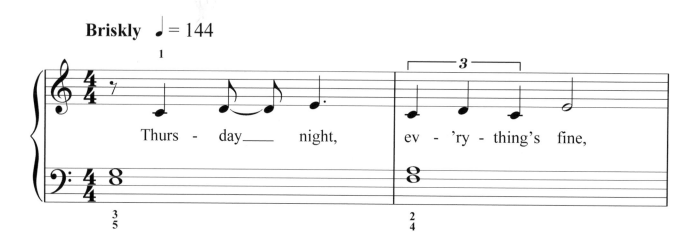

Thurs - day___ night, ev - 'ry - thing's fine,

ex - cept you've got that look in your eye. When I'm tell - ing a stor - y and

you find it bor - ing, you're think - ing of some - thing to say. You'll go a-

BLEEDING LOVE

Words & Music by Jesse McCartney & Ryan Tedder

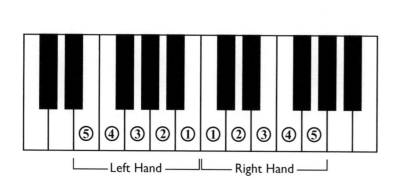

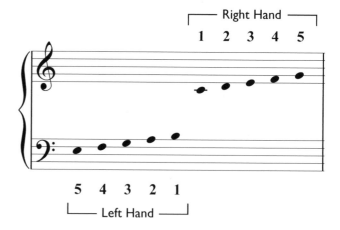

Expressively ♩ = 100

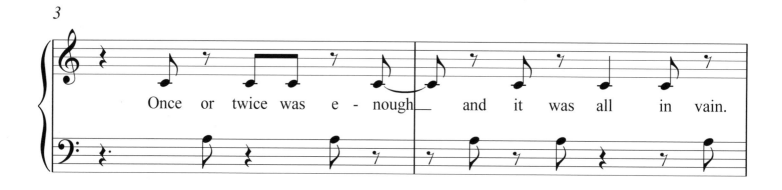

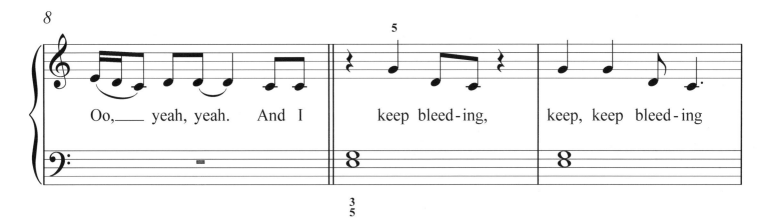

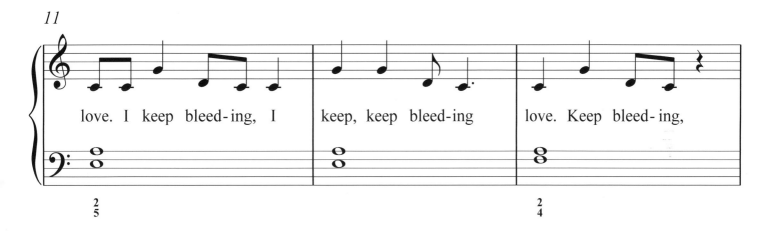

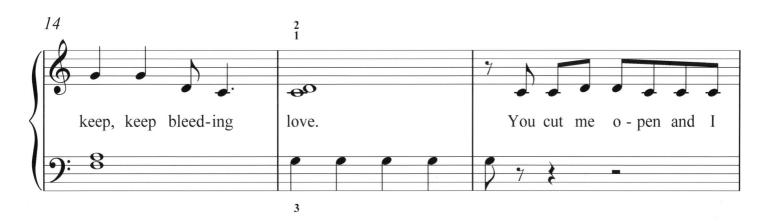

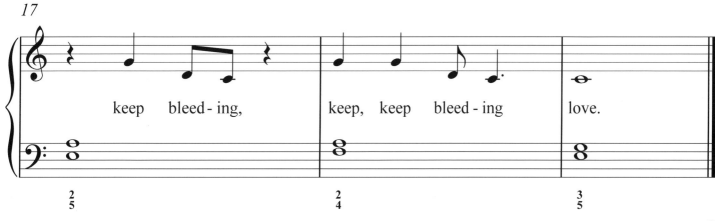

CLOCKS

Words & Music by Guy Berryman, Chris Martin, Jon Buckland & Will Champion

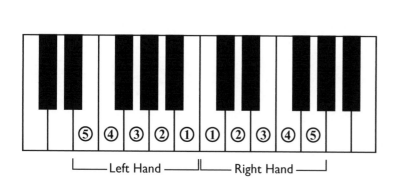

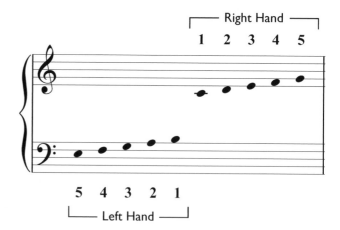

With momentum ♩ = 120

Lights go out and I can't be saved,_ tides that I tried to swim a-gainst_ brought me down up-on my knees._ Oh, I beg, I

ALWAYS WHERE I NEED TO BE

Words & Music by Luke Pritchard

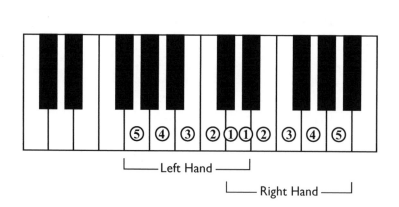

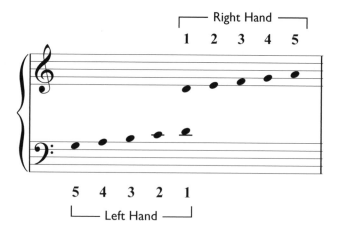

Brightly, with a bounce ♩ = 152

She don't know who___ she is, oh,

I can take her an - y - where. Do what - ev - er___ comes

nat - 'ral - ly to you, you know she just don't___ care.

CAN'T GET YOU OUT OF MY HEAD

Words & Music by Cathy Dennis & Rob Davis

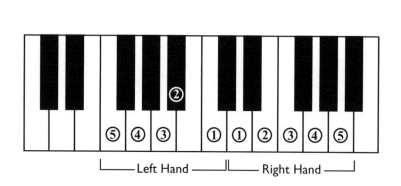

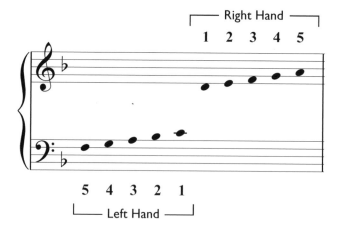

With a steady beat ♩ = 108

I just can't get you out of my head. Boy, your

lov-ing is all I think a-bout. I just can't get you out of my head. Boy, it's

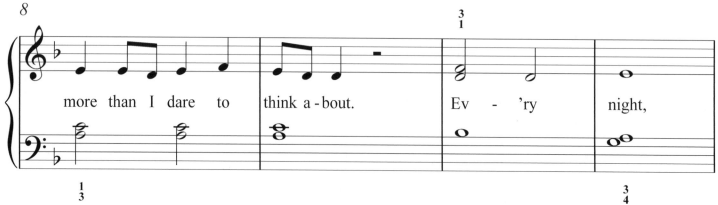

more than I dare to think a-bout. Ev-'ry night,

CHASING CARS

Words & Music by Paul Wilson, Gary Lightbody, Jonathan Quinn, Nathan Connolly & Tom Simpson

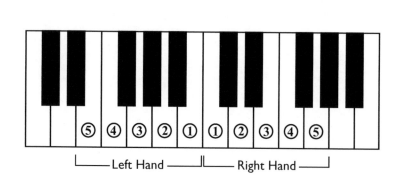 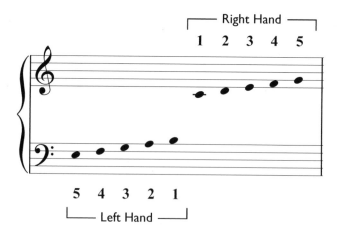

Softly ♩ = 96

We'll do it___ all,___

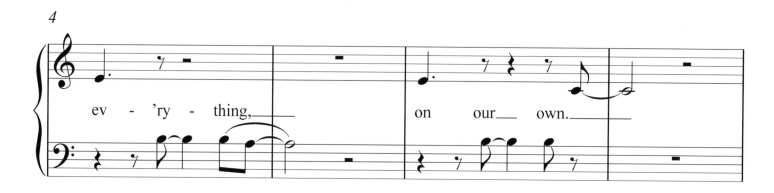

ev - 'ry - thing,___ on our___ own.___

We don't___ need___ an - y - thing___

OOPS!... I DID IT AGAIN

Words & Music by Max Martin & Rami

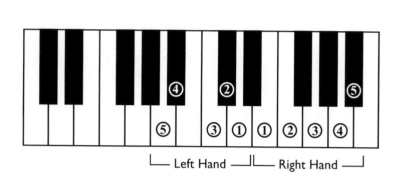

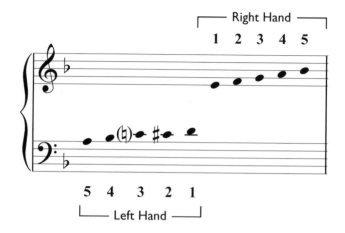

Rhythmically ♩ = 92

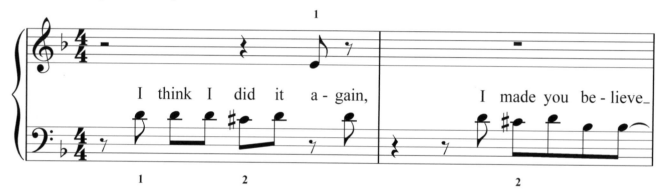

I think I did it a-gain,   I made you be-lieve

we're more than just friends.   Oh, ba-by,   it might seem like a crush,

but it does-n't mean   that I'm se-ri-ous.

EASIEST 5-FINGER
PIANO COLLECTION
ALSO AVAILABLE IN THE SERIES!

Ballads
A superb collection of 15 well-known ballads, including 'Fix You', 'I Have A Dream', 'Let It Be' and 'What A Wonderful World'.
AM995346

Film Songs
15 great film songs including 'Breaking Free', 'Don't Worry, Be Happy', 'Somewhere Out There' and 'You've Got A Friend In Me'.
AM995335

Showtunes
15 great showtunes including 'Any Dream Will Do', 'Circle Of Life', 'Mamma Mia' and 'My Favourite Things'.
AM995324

Download to your computer a set of piano accompaniments for this *Chart Hits* edition
(to be played by a teacher/parent).
Visit: **www.hybridpublications.com**
Registration is free and easy.

Your registration code is LB072

Published by
Wise Publications
14-15 Berners Street,
London W1T 3LJ, UK.

Exclusive Distributors:
Music Sales Limited
Distribution Centre, Newmarket Road,
Bury St Edmunds, Suffolk IP33 3YB, UK.
Music Sales Pty Limited
20 Resolution Drive, Caringbah,
NSW 2229, Australia.

Order No. AM995357
ISBN 978-1-84772-727-5

Edited by Fiona Bolton.
Arranged and engraved by Camden Music.

Printed in the EU.

Your Guarantee of Quality
As publishers, we strive to produce every
book to the highest commercial standards.
This book has been carefully designed to
minimise awkward page turns and to
make playing from it a real pleasure.
Particular care has been given to specifying acid-free,
neutral-sized paper made from pulps which have
not been elemental chlorine bleached.
This pulp is from farmed sustainable forests and was
produced with special regard for the environment.
Throughout, the printing and binding have been
planned to ensure a sturdy, attractive publication
which should give years of enjoyment.
If your copy fails to meet our high standards,
please inform us and we will gladly replace it.

www.musicsales.com